WIT & WISDOM OF
AKBAR & BIRBAL

Awesome Wit And Wisdom Of Akbar And Birbal
ISBN : 978-93-5049-451-6

Reprinted in 2012

Published by :

SHREE BOOK CENTRE
8, Kakad Indl Estate, S. Keer Marg, Matunga West,
Mumbai - 400016, INDIA.
Phone : 91-22-24377516 / 24374559
Telefax : 91-22-24309183
E-mail : sales@shreebookcentre.com

Printed in India

Preface

There could possibly be no child in India who hasn't heard an Akbar Birbal story. These stories have become such an integral part of our rich culture that they continue to delight children and adults even today. Your child could have a lot to learn from Birbal's wit and wisdom, his skills of perception and ability to ease difficult situations.

Large fonts have been used to make reading easy and to keep the child's interest alive. The colourful illustrations used throughout the book will keep your child glued to the end. Difficult words and their meanings have been listed at the end to enhance your child's vocabulary.

Go ahead! Start your child on an enthralling journey with Birbal and his King Akbar. Get hold of all 4 books in this collection today!

CONTENTS

1.   Birbal's Daughter   1

2.   The Bag of Coins   9

3.   Birbal Returns Home   17

4.   Birbal's Justice   25

5.   Fear is the Key   33

6.   The Loyal Gardener   41

7.   Poet Raichand   49

8.   The Real Owner   57

9.   The Royal Advisor   65

Birbal's Daughter

In Emperor Akbar's court, Birbal was respected as a very wise and witty man. His intelligence was well-known in kingdoms across the world. Akbar was very happy and proud to have Birbal as a member of his court.

The wise Birbal had a young daughter, who sometimes used to accompany him to Emperor Akbar's court. She was a bright and intelligent little girl who had captured the heart of Akbar. All the courtiers, too, were impressed by her intelligence.

One day, Emperor Akbar thought to himself, 'If Birbal is such a smart and witty man, then would his daughter also be as intelligent and clever as her father?' Akbar made up his mind that he would find out for himself.

So, the following morning, Akbar requested Birbal to bring his daughter to the court. Birbal wondered, why? The Emperor had never made such a request before. It was very strange indeed. But Birbal bowed and agreed to bring his daughter along.

Birbal brought his daughter with him to the court the next day. Akbar called her by his side and asked her if she knew how to speak the Persian language. At first, the little girl felt a bit shy and did not say anything. So, Birbal smiled at his daughter and encouraged her to speak.

The young girl smiled sweetly at the Emperor and answered. She said that she knew Persian language, a little more and a little less! Hearing the reply, Akbar was quite confused. But Birbal, who was standing close by, was smiling at his daughter proudly, as if he understood her words.

Akbar then turned to his wise minister Birbal and asked him to explain his daughter's answer. Birbal replied that his daughter meant that she knew a little more Persian than those who did not know the language at all and a little less than those who knew the language well.

Akbar roared with laughter. He immediately took off his necklace and gave it to her. He was highly impressed with Birbal's daughter. He now realised that she was just as clever as her father, Birbal, the wisest and wittiest courtier in his court.

The Bag of Coins

In Emperor Akbar's kingdom, there once lived an oil merchant, who was a wealthy and an honest man. He had a neighbour, who was a rice merchant. The rice merchant was a shrewd and dishonest man and thought only about making money in crooked ways.

One day, the oil merchant was going out of town. Since he was to be away for a long time, he did not want to leave his money at home. So, he entrusted a big bag of gold coins to his neighbour for safe keeping. The rice merchant assured the oil merchant not to worry, and that he would take good care of the moneybag.

After a long time, the oil merchant returned. He went to the rice merchant's place to ask for his gold coins. The rice merchant looked at the oil merchant with a frown and said that the bag of gold coins actually belonged to him and that the oil merchant was lying. The rice merchant refused to part with it!

The two merchants had a heated argument and then they decided to take the matter before the wise Birbal. The oil merchant was sure that only Birbal would be able to find a way to trap the crooked merchant. The two merchants soon reached Birbal's home.

Birbal listened to both the merchants as they argued. After he had heard their arguments, Birbal silenced them and said that he would find out who was the rightful owner of the gold coins. He then asked the guard standing outside to bring a tub full of water and place it on the table.

When the tub of water was brought, Birbal immersed the coins into it and then looked very closely at the water. And soon enough, a fine layer of oil was formed on the surface of the water. Birbal immediately knew that the oil merchant was the true owner and the rice merchant was a cheat.

The crooked rice merchant did not think he would get caught so easily, but thanks to clever Birbal, his lie was discovered, and the rightful owner of the coins was found. The rice merchant had to return the gold coins to the oil merchant. Birbal then ordered his guard to take the crooked merchant to prison.

The oil merchant was very happy that justice had been done. He thanked Birbal and presented him with a barrel of the best mustard oil in the kingdom, as a token of his gratitude!

Birbal Returns Home

Once, the King of Persia invited Birbal to visit his court. Birbal accepted the invitation and went to Persia. A month later, he returned. The next day, he came to Akbar's court. Akbar was very pleased to meet Birbal after such a long time.

The Emperor was full of questions. He was also very keen to know what the King of Persia was like. So, he asked Birbal details about the Persian King. And, Akbar also wanted to know who was a better emperor and ruler –the King of Persia or he himself?

Birbal was surprised by the Emperor's query. He thought about the question for a few moments and then gave his answer. He said that if he was to compare the two kings, he thought the King of Persia was like a full moon, whereas Emperor Akbar was more like a new moon.

Hearing Birbal's statement, the Emperor was terribly upset. He was shocked that his most loyal courtier, who he admired so much, would say such a terrible thing about him!

Birbal realised that Akbar was unhappy with his comment, so he quickly explained the meaning of what he was saying. He said that the Persian King was like the full moon, because his powers were declining. A full moon can only get smaller and smaller in size. So, like the full moon, the Persian Emperor was losing his power.

Birbal then explained that, on the other hand, the new moon could only grow in size. Just like Emperor Akbar's kingdom and powers, which were growing from strength to strength every day and spreading their radiance all around.

Emperor Akbar was satisfied with Birbal's explanation. His face beamed with happiness. He really admired his minister Birbal and his opinion mattered a lot to him. Akbar was greatly relieved that the wise Birbal believed that he was a better King than the King of Persia.

Emperor Akbar then decided to throw a large feast in honour of Birbal's visit to Persia. All the people in the kingdom were invited to join in the feast. And there was a special ceremony to felicitate the wise Birbal. He was touched to see such a grand welcome and was very happy to be back home.

Birbal's Justice

There was a rich and successful merchant who lived in Emperor Akbar's kingdom. The merchant kept all his gold and important documents in a locker in his chamber. One morning, he discovered that someone had broken into the locker and stolen all the gold!

The merchant was shocked, for he lived in a large mansion and had many servants working for him. He was quite sure that the culprit had to be someone who knew where he kept his gold. It could be any one of the servants, he felt, but he did not know how to find the thief.

The only person wise enough to solve the mystery of the missing gold was Birbal, the minister. So, the very next day, the merchant went to Birbal and begged for his help. After hearing his story, Birbal agreed to help the merchant and assured him that he would catch the culprit within a day.

The merchant returned to his mansion along with Birbal to solve the crime. Birbal knew that he would have to think of a clever way to trap the thief. So, he called all the servants together. When they all arrived in front of him, he gave them a wooden stick each.

After the sticks were distributed to each of the servants, Birbal, then, instructed the servants to keep the sticks with them for the night. He told the servants that these sticks were no ordinary sticks but were magical ones. He also said that the culprit's stick would grow by an inch overnight.

The next morning, Birbal called all the servants before him and asked to see each of their sticks. He had a close look at all the sticks. He noticed that one stick was an inch shorter than the rest. Birbal told the merchant that the servant with the shorter stick was the thief.

30

Birbal then revealed that there was nothing magical about the sticks; they were just ordinary wooden sticks! He knew that the servant who had robbed the merchant of his precious gold would cut the stick by one inch, so that he would not be caught. And he did exactly that, and was caught!

The servant who had robbed the gold broke down and confessed that he was indeed the thief. He also promised his master that he would return all the gold. The rich merchant was overjoyed and could not stop thanking Birbal for his invaluable help.

Fear is the Key

Akbar and Birbal were strolling in the royal gardens one day. Akbar said to Birbal that he believed all his subjects loved him, as they were very obedient and loyal. Birbal smiled and replied that Akbar's subjects did indeed love him, but they also feared him.

Emperor Akbar was quite surprised and taken aback with his loyal minister's statement. He did not expect his favourite minister to say something so grave, so he decided to see if there was any truth in it. He made a plan to test whether his subjects obeyed him out of love or out of fear.

The next day, when the court was in session, Akbar made an announcement. He said that he would be going out on a hunting trip to the nearby forest in the morning and ordered all the people in his kingdom to pour a small pot of milk into the tub in his palace courtyard by the evening.

Since Akbar was out hunting, people did not bother to put milk into the tub and put water instead. When Emperor Akbar returned in the evening, tired from his hunt, he was disappointed to find that the tub was overflowing with water and not milk!

Once again, Emperor Akbar made an announcement in the kingdom, ordering his subjects to pour a small pot of milk into the tub in the royal courtyard. He also made it very clear to them that this time he would come personally and check if there was milk in the tub or not.

Now, hearing this announcement, the people of Akbar's kingdom did not wish to upset their Emperor. The next day, when Akbar left for the hunt, the people quickly brought their pots of milk and poured them into the tub. This time no one poured any water.

That evening, when Akbar returned from the hunt, he went straight to look at the tub. He saw that it was filled to the brim with milk. Akbar had to admit that what Birbal had said was true. His subjects did love him, but they obeyed him out of fear.

Emperor Akbar was very happy. Once again, Birbal had proved that he was wise and clever. As a reward for his wisdom, the overjoyed Emperor Akbar gifted his favourite minister a new mansion, a beautiful white stallion and several bags of gold.

The Loyal Gardener

One evening, Emperor Akbar was taking a walk in the royal garden, when he accidentally stumbled upon a small rock. Akbar was in a very bad mood that day. He summoned the gardener and sentenced him to death for not having removed the stone.

The poor gardener was distraught at receiving such a harsh sentence. He pleaded with the Emperor but Akbar was adamant. The gardener did not know what to do. He ran to Birbal in despair and begged him to find a way to save his life.

The gardener told Birbal the entire story. Birbal wondered how he could help the poor gardener. He pondered for a while and finally thought of a way. He told the gardener not to worry, and then whispered some instructions in his ear.

The next day, Emperor Akbar was walking in his royal garden again. The gardener came up to the Emperor and spat at his feet! The Emperor was shocked at this. He was furious to see the same gardener commit such an act of disrespect.

Just then, Birbal walked up to the Emperor. Akbar was even more surprised to discover that Birbal had instructed the gardener to spit on his feet. Seeing that the Emperor was furious, Birbal then explained to him as to why the gardener had done such a deed.

Birbal told the Emperor that the gardener was one of the most loyal subjects who served the King. And it would have been a shame on the Emperor's part for sentencing a man to death for such a petty reason as forgetting to remove a small rock.

And, therefore, Birbal had asked the gardener to spit at Akbar's feet. That was a vile offence and would give Emperor Akbar a genuine reason to sentence him to death. The Emperor was stunned by the whole incident and he instantly realised his mistake and forgave the gardener.

The loyal gardener fell at Birbal's feet and thanked him for saving his life. Emperor Akbar was also very grateful and thanked Birbal profusely for making him realise his folly and for stopping him from committing a serious blunder. Once again, Birbal had saved the day with his intelligence.

Poet Raichand

In Agra, there lived a rich merchant, who was very miserly. Now this miserly merchant was very fond of poetry. One day, it so happened that a poet called Raichand came to the merchant's house and offered to read his poems to him. The merchant agreed.

Poet Raichand recited his wonderful poetry. He had even composed one poem especially for the merchant. The merchant praised Raichand and showered him with flowery words. At the end of the recital, the merchant was very pleased and asked Raichand to return the next day to collect his reward.

The next day, Poet Raichand came to the merchant's house to receive his reward. The miserly merchant pretended that he had never promised Raichand any gift or reward. Raichand was taken aback and was very upset. He went to his friend Birbal for help.

Birbal heard his friend's story and offered to help him. "We will teach the merchant a lesson," he told Raichand. He asked Raichand to invite the rich merchant for a grand feast to his place. The merchant readily accepted the invitation to the feast, as he loved eating good food.

On the day of the feast, the merchant arrived at Raichand's house. To his surprise, he noticed that he was the only guest invited. Raichand greeted his guest very warmly. The merchant was quite hungry and hoped that Raichand would serve dinner soon.

But, Raichand kept talking to him and did not serve any food! This went on the whole evening. Finally, at midnight, the merchant was so hungry that he could not bear it and asked Raichand to serve dinner. Raichand pretended as if he did not know what the merchant was talking about.

The merchant realised that Poet Raichand was teaching him a lesson, because he too had pretended that he did not know Raichand just a few days earlier. The rich merchant felt very ashamed of his behaviour and immediately took off his expensive necklace and gifted it to Raichand.

Poet Raichand marvelled at his friend Birbal's wisdom. He was happy that the merchant had repented and learned his lesson. He served dinner to his hungry guest and they both ate a happy meal together. Thus, Birbal's wisdom helped a simple poet get what he deserved.

The Real Owner

A merchant was once riding to Delhi on some urgent work. On the way, he came upon a traveller who seemed like he was lame. The merchant halted near the traveller and being kind-hearted, he offered the man a ride on his horse and he himself dismounted.

Thus, they travelled together. Once they reached Delhi, the merchant asked the man to get off, as he needed to travel further for his work. The traveller, however, refused to get off the horse and started claiming that he was the merchant and that the horse rightfully belonged to him!

This led to an argument between the two men and they started fighting in the middle of the road. Soon, a crowd gathered around to watch the fight. One of the men in the crowd, who tried to pacify them, suggested that they take the matter to Birbal.

The merchant and the lame man went to Birbal for help. The merchant told the whole story and accused the man of trying to steal his identity and his horse. The traveller, in turn, accused the merchant of the same thing.

Birbal pondered over the problem for a moment. He then hit upon a plan on how to find the real owner. He had the horse sent to the royal stables. And then, Birbal asked the traveller and the merchant to follow him to the stables.

Once they reached the stables, Birbal asked both the men to identify the horse that they were claiming they owned. The lame traveller, of course, was unable to recognise the horse, as it did not belong to him at all. There were so many horses in the stable and they all looked similar!

When the merchant was asked to identify his horse, he could do it immediately. He joyfully patted his horse's head and the horse neighed at his master. That was enough evidence to convince Birbal as to who was the real owner. Birbal had, thus, solved the case.

The rogue traveller was immediately arrested for cheating and taken off to jail by Birbal's guards. The merchant was very grateful to Birbal for resolving the problem so easily. He was happy to have his faithful horse back and so he presented Birbal with a huge reward.

The Royal Advisor

It was time for Emperor Akbar to appoint his royal advisor. Akbar knew that there was only one candidate worthy of the position – Birbal. But, he also knew that all his other courtiers desperately wanted the position as well. This put him in a tricky situation.

So, Emperor Akbar decided to give all his courtiers a test. The next day, in court, Akbar announced that he would like to test the mental skills of all his courtiers through a task. And the person who successfully completed the task would be appointed as his royal advisor.

Akbar gave his courtiers a piece of cloth. He told his courtiers that they must try and cover him from head to toe with the cloth. Then, Emperor Akbar lay down on a divan, waiting to be covered.

One by one, each of the courtiers tried to cover the Emperor with the piece of cloth that he had given them. And to their dismay, they all failed. There was one problem. The piece of cloth was not long enough to cover the Emperor fully from head to toe.

If the cloth covered Akbar's head, his feet would be uncovered. If his feet were covered then his head would be uncovered. This was a real problem. The courtiers tried their best, but in vain. Finally, the tired courtiers gave up, declaring that it was an impossible task.

Finally, Emperor Akbar summoned his favourite minister, Birbal, and gave him the same piece of cloth and the same task. Birbal took the cloth with a smile. Akbar lay down on the divan, just as he had done before and waited for Birbal to cover him.

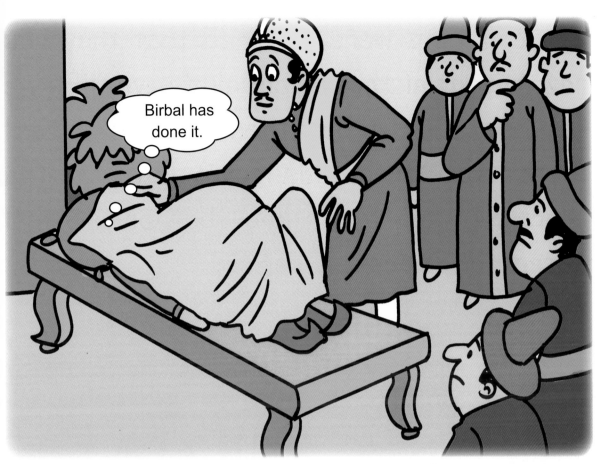

Before Birbal covered Akbar, he made a simple request. He asked Emperor Akbar to lift his knees and pull his feet closer to his body. Akbar did as he was asked to do. Birbal then placed the cloth over the Emperor and covered him fully from head to toe.

The courtiers were ashamed that they had not thought of the clever solution that Birbal had. Emperor Akbar then announced that Birbal was to be his royal advisor. The courtiers had to accept that only Birbal deserved the post.

MEANINGS OF DIFFICULT WORDS

Birbal's Daughter

accompany – go with someone

impressed – moved or excited

The Bag of Coins

shrewd   – crafty and clever

assured   – made sure

Birbal Returns Home

query   – question

felicitate – congratulate or praise

MEANINGS OF DIFFICULT WORDS

Birbal's Justice

Confessed	– admitted to the truth
invaluable	– of great value

Fear is the Key

Feared	- Be afraid of
Grave	- Serious
Disappointed	- Felt let down
Personally	- In person, himself
Overjoyed	- Very happy

The Loyal Gardener

distraught	– disturbed or upset
adamant	– firm or rigid in behaviour
despair	– sadness or misery
furious	– very angry
petty	– unimportant
vile	– wicked

MEANINGS OF DIFFICULT WORDS

Poet Raichand

merchant   – trader

ashamed   – sorry

marveled   – was amazed or surprised

Repented   – was sorry for one's mistakes

The Real Owner

Lame   – with deformed legs

Pacify   – calm down

accused   – blamed

pondered   – thought about

evidence   – proof

The Royal Advisor

worthy   – deserving

Divan   – Indian word for sofa

Dismay   – fear